# Alf Prøysen

Mrs Pepperpot

Turns Detective

PENGUIN BOOKS

PENGUIN BOOKS

Published by the Penguin Group
Penguin Books Ltd, 27 Wrights Lane, London w8 5tz, England
Penguin Books USA Inc., 375 Hudson Street, New York, New York 10014, USA
Penguin Books Australia Ltd, Ringwood, Victoria, Australia
Penguin Books Canada Ltd, 10 Alcorn Avenue, Toronto, Ontario, Canada m4v 3b2
Penguin Books (NZ) Ltd, 182–190 Wairau Road, Auckland 10, New Zealand

Penguin Books Ltd, Registered Offices: Harmondsworth, Middlesex, England

**First published in *Mrs Pepperpot in the Magic Wood and Other Stories***
**by Hutchinson Junior Books Ltd 1968**
**Published in Puffin Books 1972**

This collection published in Penguin Books 1996
1 3 5 7 9 10 8 6 4 2

Copyright © Alf Prøysen, 1968

This translation copyright © Hutchinson Junior Books Ltd, 1968
All rights reserved

The moral right of the author has been asserted

Set in 12.5/13pt Bembo Monotype
Typeset by Datix International Limited, Bungay, Suffolk
Printed in England by Clays Ltd, St Ives plc

# Contents

# Mrs Pepperpot in the Magic Wood

MRS PEPPERPOT, as you may remember, lives on a hillside in Norway. Behind her house there is an old fence with a gate in it. If you walk through that gate, says Mrs Pepperpot, you walk straight into the Magic Wood.

It's really just a little copse with larch and spruce and birch trees, but in spring the ground is covered with snowdrops – the whitest carpet you ever saw, and round a big mossy stone a patch of violets make a bright splash of colour. The birch trees seem more silvery in here and the pale green branches of the larch trees more feathery as they sway over the stream that trickles down the hillside. And in and out of the long grass the weasel has made a pattern of little winding paths. It is very beautiful.

But Mrs Pepperpot likes it even better in winter when the Magic Wood has a thick carpet of snow and the icicles sparkle from the branches. Then all is silent except for the scrunch, scrunch of Mrs Pepperpot's boots as she walks through the snow.

It was a day before Christmas, and Mrs Pepperpot had asked her husband to cut her a small Christmas tree in the Magic Wood. But he was so busy at his work that he hadn't time to do it, so Mrs Pepperpot decided to take the axe and cut it down herself. As the snow was slippery, she took a stick with her. She soon reached the little fir-tree and, after marking a circle round it with her stick, she lifted the axe to start chopping.

Then the awful thing happened! You know, the thing that keeps happening to Mrs Pepperpot at the most inconvenient moments: she shrank to the size of a pepperpot.

'I'll have to find a small stick,' she said, 'it'll help me to plough a path through the snow. Ah well, I could be in a worse fix, I suppose, and I ought to be used to it by now.'

'Hi!' shouted a small voice quite close above her.

'What was that?' said Mrs Pepperpot, who had nearly jumped out of her skin, she was so surprised.

'It's me!' said the little voice. And now Mrs Pepperpot could see a tiny boy no bigger than herself, standing by her side.

2    'Well, come on; don't just stand there! They're

all sitting inside, crying their hearts out because they think the ogre has eaten you. We must hurry home and surprise them.'

Without waiting for an answer, the little fellow bent down to a hole in the snow and started to crawl into it.

'Well,' thought Mrs Pepperpot, 'I may as well go and see what this is all about; he seems to know me, even if I don't know him.'

She left the axe and tucking the stick she had found under her arm she bravely crawled after the boy into the hole. It was quite a long tunnel which led to a little door. The boy knocked, but from behind the door there was such a noise of wailing and weeping that at first no one answered his knock. But when he had knocked again the bolt slid back and the door was opened by a young girl with a ladle in her hand. The room was brightly lit by a fire over which hung a steaming pot. Mrs Pepperpot, who was hidden behind the boy in the dark tunnel, could see three people inside and they were all looking most dejected as they went on with their crying.

The little boy stamped his foot. 'Stop that noise!' he shouted. 'Can't you see I've brought 3

Betty Bodkin back?' and with that he took hold of Mrs Pepperpot's arm and dragged her into the middle of the room.

For a moment everyone stared at Mrs Pepperpot and then the wailing began afresh!

'Little Dick, what have you done? This isn't Betty Bodkin!' said the girl with the ladle.

Little Dick turned and had a good look at Mrs Pepperpot. Then he shook his fists at her and threw himself on the floor in what can only be described as a temper tantrum.

But Mrs Pepperpot had had enough of this nonsense: 'When you've all finished your cata-wauling,' she said, 'perhaps someone will tell me who you are and who I'm *supposed* to be. Then maybe I'll tell you who I *really* am.'

'It is a bit confusing,' said a fat little man who sat nearest the fire, 'we thought you were one of us, you see.'

'So I hear, but who are *you*?' Mrs Pepperpot was losing patience.

'Let me explain,' said the girl with the ladle, and as no one tried to stop her, she continued: 'You may not recognize us, but when you were little you knew us well enough. D'you re-member your mother taking you on her lap sometimes to cut your nails? You probably didn't like it, and she would hold your hand and count your fingers one by one.'

'That's right,' said Mrs Pepperpot, 'and then she would sing me a little ditty that went like this:

> *Here is Thumbkin, fat and tubby,*
> *Here is Lickpot, always grubby,*
> *Longman next: he has his fiddle,*
> *Now Betty Bodkin with her needle,*
> *And little Dick who's just a tiddle.'*

They all clapped their hands. 'There you are!' cried the girl, 'you haven't forgotten. And that's who we are – the finger people who live in the Magic Wood. This is Thumbkin,' she said, pointing to the fat little man by the fire.

'Pleased to meet you,' said Thumbkin, as Mrs Pepperpot shook hands with him.

'I used to find you a very comforting person,' said Mrs Pepperpot smiling.

'This is Longman, as you can see,' went on the girl, but the tall, thin fellow was so shy he held his fiddle behind his back and looked as if he'd like to vanish right away. 'I'm Lickpot. I do the cooking, you see,' said the girl.

Little Dick had now got over his disappointment. Taking another look at Mrs Pepperpot he said: 'You're so very like Betty Bodkin!'

'Just what happened to Betty Bodkin?' asked Mrs Pepperpot.

Immediately they all started talking at once: 'It was like this – we were out in the wood – we always wish the moon a Happy Christmas – it was such a glorious night!'

'One at a time, please!' said Mrs Pepperpot, holding her ears.

Lickpot raised her ladle to get order: 'Quiet now! I'll explain. As they said, we went for a walk to greet the moon. Suddenly a huge ogre came along the path and we all had to rush into the tunnel to get out of his way. But Betty Bodkin tripped over her needle, and didn't manage it. The ogre picked her up in his great hand and put her in his pocket. Now we're all so worried about what has happened to her, and Christmas won't be Christmas without Betty Bodkin!'

'Perhaps the ogre has eaten her up!' said Little Dick, and he started to cry again.

'Oh, ogres aren't as bad as they once were!' said Mrs Pepperpot to comfort him. 'Besides, if she's as used to being small as I am, she'll know how to get out of tight corners.'

'If only we could find where the ogre lives, then perhaps we could rescue her,' said Lickpot.

'I'm sure we could, if we all pull together,' said Mrs Pepperpot. 'I think I have an idea where that ogre lives.'

'Will you show us the way?' asked Little Dick excitedly, and they all crowded round Mrs Pepperpot, tugging at her skirt.

'There's no time to lose,' she said and immediately started crawling back through the tunnel. The others followed, but when they got outside they found the road blocked by an enormous snowdrift.

'We'll never get through that!' said Thumbkin and looked quite ready to creep back inside to his warm fire.

It was quite a problem, and Mrs Pepperpot shut her eyes so as to think better. Suddenly she remembered something very important: they were in the Magic Wood, where wishes come true if you wish hard enough. 'Quiet, everybody! I'm going to make a wish!' she said.

While they all stood very still she touched the snowdrift with her stick and said loudly: 'I wish 7 this snowdrift to turn into a polar bear – a *friendly* polar bear – who can carry us all on his back and take us to the ogre's house.'

As soon as she finished speaking the snowdrift began to rise under them and they found themselves sitting on a soft, warm, white rug. Then the rug began to move forward, and Mrs Pepperpot could see two ears in front of her. She had ridden on a bear before, so she knew what bears like most – to be tickled between the ears. Gingerly she crawled towards the ears and perched herself between them.

'Do be careful!' warned Lickpot, who was clinging with all her might to the bear's fur. Longman was so frightened he was lying full length with his face buried, but Thumbkin and Little Dick were beginning to enjoy themselves, looking all around from their high seat.

When the bear felt his ears being tickled he purred – or rather, he rumbled – with contentment, and in no time at all he had carried Mrs Pepperpot and the finger people to the edge of the wood where there was a fence and a gate in it.

'Open the gate with your muzzle!' commanded Mrs Pepperpot, and the big polar bear did just as she said and opened the gate.

Then they came to a house with a lighted window.

'Now I want you to lie down outside the door,' said Mrs Pepperpot, 'and you must wait there till I come out again — is that clear?'

The great creature just nodded his head slowly and settled down on the doorstep.

Mrs Pepperpot turned to the finger people: 'I'm pretty certain that I'll find the ogre inside this house,' she said.

'Don't you want us to help you rescue Betty Bodkin?' asked Little Dick, who was feeling quite chirpy now.

'No thanks, I think I can manage this by myself,' said Mrs Pepperpot. 'I just want you to wait here with Mr Polar Bear. If Betty Bodkin is there I'll bring her out to you, and then you can all go home.'

They all shook her hand warmly and wished her luck.

'Trust in me!' said Mrs Pepperpot, and swung her leg over the door-sill.

Just as she disappeared into the dark hall she grew to her normal size and walked into the dining-room.

There sat Mr Pepperpot; the tears were rolling

down his cheeks and his sharp nose was quite red with crying. On the table by his side stood a small doll's bed Mrs Pepperpot had bought to give a little girl for Christmas, and in the bed lay Betty Bodkin, trying very hard to look like a doll! There were medicine bottles on the table as well, and a box of liquorice pills.

Mrs Pepperpot put her hands on her hips and said: 'Just what are you carrying on like this for?'

At the sound of her voice Mr Pepperpot looked up. He couldn't believe his eyes!

'Is that you? Is that really you, my own wife?' he cried, and caught hold of her skirt to see if she wasn't a ghost. 'I thought I'd lost you this time! I was going through the wood, searching for you, when I saw . . .' He stopped and stared at the little old woman in the doll's bed. 'But then, who's this? I picked her up in the snow and brought her home, thinking it was you who had shrunk again.'

'You silly man! Mixing me up with a doll that someone has dropped on the path!' said Mrs Pepperpot. Then, standing between him and the doll's bed, she carefully lifted Betty Bodkin up and wiped away the sticky medicine and liquor-
10 ice pills her husband had tried to dose her with.

Betty was just about to thank her, but Mrs Pepperpot made a sign for her to keep quiet and carried her towards the front door.

But Mr Pepperpot was so afraid his wife might vanish once more that he followed, holding on to her coat. As she leaned out of the door he asked: 'What are you putting the doll in that snowdrift for?'

'To get her back where she belongs,' said Mrs Pepperpot. 'Come and have your supper now.'

'Just a minute. I want to shovel that snowdrift away from the door-step first,' Mr Pepperpot said.

'Why? Are you afraid it'll walk in? Come on now, supper's ready.'

So Mr Pepperpot went into the kitchen to wash his hands and didn't hear his wife whisper to the snowdrift: 'Turn about, quick march and get them home as fast as you can!'

Later that night, when she was washing up, Mrs Pepperpot amused herself by singing the old ditty:

> *Here is Thumbkin, fat and tubby,*
> *Here is Lickpot, always grubby,*
> *Longman next: he has a fiddle,*
> *Now Betty Bodkin with her needle,*
> *And Little Dick who's just a tiddle.*

# Mrs Pepperpot Turns Detective

MRS PEPPERPOT has tried her hand at many jobs, but this autumn she has tried something new – she has turned detective.

Of all the seasons Mrs Pepperpot likes autumn best. When anyone complains that it's dark and dreary, she always answers that it's the best time of the year, because then we get the reward for all the hard work we put in in the spring with our digging and sowing and planting.

'But the days get so short and the nights get so long!' they say.

'That makes it all the cosier indoors,' says Mrs Pepperpot, 'and think of all the fun the children have, playing detectives with torches in the dark.'

'All right, but what about the burglars and such-like? They have a much better chance to do their stealing at this time of year.'

So the argument ran, but Mrs Pepperpot said no more, because, you see, someone had been stealing from *her*, and she very much wanted to play detective herself.

And what d'you think was being stolen from Mrs Pepperpot? Her potatoes, of all things! Ever since September, when she first started digging them up, she had been finding plants with no potatoes under them; they had been dug up, the potatoes taken off and then the plants stuck back in the soil to make them look as if they were still growing. Wasn't that a cunning trick?

Mrs Pepperpot couldn't think who it could be. If only she were a *real* detective, then she could trace footprints in the mud, perhaps even fingerprints on the leaves of the potato-plants. She could build a secret observation post and carry a gun, and when she had caught the thief red-handed, she would say: 'Hands up!'

At supper one night she was thinking so hard about being a detective that she said 'Hands up!' when she was passing a bowl of hot stew to her husband, and he dropped it all over the clean table-cloth in his fright. For once she couldn't very well scold him.

After supper she remembered she had left her potato bucket out in the field almost full of potatoes. 'I'd better fetch it in, or the thief might take that too,' she thought.

She put a scarf round her head and found the torch, for it was a very dark night. Then she went out to the field and was just bending down to pick up the bucket when she heard someone climbing through the hedge. Quickly she put out the torch and got right down on her knees over the bucket, so that she couldn't be seen.

'I'll catch him this time!' she said to herself and her heart was going pitterpat with excitement! But was she *cross* a moment later, when she found herself sprawling among the potatoes in the bucket; she had SHRUNK, of course.

It wasn't even any good trying to climb out of the bucket; because how could she get through all that mud back to the house while she was tiny? And she did so want to catch the thief! So, there was nothing for it but to lie where she was and try and see what the thief looked like.

First she listened very carefully; there was someone climbing through the hedge, right enough. But what was that? Two more people seemed to be coming through, and they were not being very quiet about it, either! Now she could hear them whispering to each other: 'Mind how you go!' This was a *boy's* voice.

'I had to pull him through the hedge!' answered a *girl's* voice.

14    'She hurt me!' wailed another younger voice.

'Ssh!' whispered the big boy, 'or we'll go straight home and not get any potatoes tonight!'

Mrs Pepperpot could hear them coming down one of the rows with a spade. They also had a bucket which rattled. The steps stopped. Now she could hear the spade going into the soil.

'Look, Sis,' said the big boy's voice, 'these are wopping great potatoes. Hold the bucket!'

The smaller child's footsteps started coming in Mrs Pepperpot's direction and in another moment he had found her bucket.

'Tum here, tum here!' he called in a high baby voice, quite forgetting he had promised to keep quiet.

'What is it?' hissed the big boy. 'Don't shout!'

But the little boy went on: 'Lots o' 'tatoes in a bucket!' he announced.

'I'll give you lots o' 'tatoes in a bucket!' muttered Mrs Pepperpot to herself; 'I'll have you all three arrested when I get back to my proper size.'

Then, as quietly as she could, she worked her way down under the top layer of potatoes, so that the children wouldn't see her. It was only just in time, as the big boy and the girl came over to have a look, and they were so pleased with 15 little brother's find that the big boy lifted up the bucket and made for the hedge.

'You carry the other bucket,' whispered the big boy to the little one, 'it's not so heavy.'

'I dood! I dood!' piped the little fellow who couldn't say his 'k's' and 'g's'. 'I find lots o' 'tatoes!' and he scrambled after the others, dragging the lighter bucket after him.

'It's a good thing it's so dark,' said the big boy, as they all got through the hedge on to the path, 'no one can see us here.'

The girl shivered a little: 'I feel like a real burglar in a detective story,' she said.

'I burgle-burgle,' chimed in the little one.

'Burglars don't usually carry detectives around in buckets!' said Mrs Pepperpot to herself. 'Just you wait, my fine friends!'

At last the children stopped at a door. They knocked and called: 'Open the door, Mother, and see what we've brought!'

The door opened and Mrs Pepperpot heard a woman's voice say: 'My! That's a fine bucketful; it'll keep us well fed for days. I'll heat the water in the pot straight away.'

'I ha' some too!' shouted the youngest, showing her the big potatoes in his bucket.

16

'Two buckets! That means you've taken one that doesn't belong to us. One of you'll have to take it back when you've eaten.'

'But, Mother!' said the boy.

'There's no "but" about it,' said his mother firmly. 'We may be so poor we have to help ourselves to a few potatoes now and then, but I hope to make it up to the owner of that field before too long. The bucket goes straight back!'

Mrs Pepperpot could hardly believe her ears; here was a family right on her door-step, so to speak, and she didn't know they were going hungry. They must be new to the neighbourhood, or surely someone would have helped them. Well, she would certainly let them have whatever potatoes they needed, no doubt about that. She had almost forgotten she was being a detective and a doll's size one at that, when the mother started lifting the potatoes out of the bucket to put them in the saucepan, which was now bubbling on the stove.

Poor Mrs Pepperpot! What should she do?

'A fine thing!' she said to herself, burrowing deeper and deeper into the bucket to hide herself. 'Here I am, being sorry for them because 17 they're poor, when I ought to be sorry for myself, going to be boiled alive any minute now!'

At last all the potatoes were in the pot and only Mrs Pepperpot was left, but by now she was so covered in earth that the mother didn't notice her.

But the little boy did. He was peering into the bucket, and he put his small hand in and lifted Mrs Pepperpot out.

'That's torn it!' said Mrs Pepperpot and shut her eyes.

'What a funny li'l 'tato!' said the little boy. 'I teep it.' And he ran off with her into the scullery, where he hid behind the door. The rest of the family were too taken up with getting the meal ready to notice where he went.

Sitting on a box, the little boy held Mrs Pepperpot very carefully on his knee.

'You my 'tato?' he asked.

Mrs Pepperpot nodded: 'That's right. I'm your 'tato.'

The little boy's eyes grew round with amazement. 'You *talking* 'tato?' he asked.

'That's right,' said Mrs Pepperpot again. 'I'm a
18 talking 'tato.'

'Tan I eat you?' he asked, looking at her very closely.

Mrs Pepperpot shivered a bit, but she spoke very calmly: 'I don't think I would, if I were you, sonny. I don't make very good eating.'

Just then his mother called him to eat his dinner. So he put Mrs Pepperpot down on the box and said: 'I ha' dinner now. You my talking 'tato – you stay here I – tum back soon play wi' you.'

'Well, sonny,' said Mrs Pepperpot, 'I may have to go, but I'll come back tomorrow and then I'll bring you a present. How's that?'

'You bring me 'nother talking 'tato!' he said and ran back to his mother who was putting a great heap of mashed potato on his plate.

Mrs Pepperpot wondered what she should do next. If she climbed back into the bucket and waited for a ride home in that, it might take hours before the boy went back to the field, and Mr Pepperpot would be fretting about her. Just then there was a little scratching noise behind the box and a mouse peeped out.

'Hullo,' said Mrs Pepperpot in mouse-language.

The mouse came out to look at her, and Mrs Pepperpot had never seen such a skinny creature. 19

'If you'll help me get out of here,' she said, 'I have a nice piece of bacon at home you can have.'

The mouse pricked up its ears. 'Bacon, did you say? We haven't seen bacon in this house for a very long time.'

'Why d'you stay here if there's so little to eat?' asked Mrs Pepperpot, as she got on the mouse's back.

'Well,' said the mouse, starting off through a hole in the wall, 'I've been with the family all my life, you know, so I don't like to leave them in the lurch. I mean, what would people say if they found out there wasn't enough food here to feed a mouse?'

When they got to the foot of the hill leading to her house, Mrs Pepperpot thanked the mouse and promised to put the piece of bacon behind the box in the scullery the next day. Then she very conveniently grew large and hurried on home.

Mr Pepperpot was standing at the front door, anxiously peering out into the dark. 'Where have you been all this time?' he asked.

'Looking for my bucket of potatoes,' said Mrs Pepperpot. 'Can't you see how grubby I am?

Crawling on my hands and knees in the mud I was, but I couldn't find it anywhere.'

Did the boy bring back the bucket? Did Mrs Pepperpot have the children arrested? And what about the little boy's talking 'tato? Well, all that is part of another story.

# Mrs Pepperpot and the Puppet Show

IT was a lovely summer's day, just the day for an outing. The village sewing club had been invited to a television show in the nearest town and they were going by special coach.

Mrs Pepperpot was going too, and very excited she was, as she had never watched a TV show in a theatre before. Nor had any of the others, for that matter, and they had all put on their best summer frocks and straw hats with flowers.

On the way they prattled, as women do, and wondered what it would be like. They were going to see a puppet show, and Sarah South was sure that everyone else in the village would be envying them.

When they got to the town the bus stopped in the market square and they all got off. As they walked into the hall Norah North said: 'One thing we shouldn't do – smile at the camera – it looks so silly when you're watching TV.'

'Especially if you have gaps in your teeth,' said

Mrs East, who could be a bit sharp when she liked.

They felt rather shy when they were given the front row of seats, but soon they were all comfortably seated with little bags of peppermints to munch. All except Mrs Pepperpot. Where was she?

Well, you know how she likes to poke her nose into things, and as they were walking along the passage to their seats, Mrs Pepperpot heard someone sniffing and crying in a little room next to the stage.

'That's funny!' she thought and peeped through the door. There she saw a full grown man with a top hat and long mustachios, sitting on a chair, crying like a baby.

'Well, I never!' said Mrs Pepperpot, but before she had time to follow the rest of her party, she SHRANK!

As she stood there, a tiny figure by the door in her bright summer dress and little straw hat, the puppet-man saw her at once. Quick as a knife he stretched out his hand and picked her up.

'*There* you are!' he said, holding her tightly between finger and thumb. 'I thought I'd lost you!'

Mrs Pepperpot was so terrified she didn't move, but when the man had had a closer look he said: 'But you're *not* my Sleeping Beauty puppet at all!'

'Of course I'm not!' said Mrs Pepperpot. The very idea!

'All the same,' said the puppet-man, 'as I can't find my most important puppet, you'll have to play her part. You'll look fine with a blonde wig and a crown and a veil, and I'll make your face up so that you'll be really beautiful.'

'You let me go this minute!' shouted Mrs Pepperpot, struggling to get out of the man's grip. 'Who ever heard of an old woman like me playing Sleeping Beauty?'

'Now, now! You have talent – you can act, I'm sure of it. And that's more than can be said of my other puppets who have to be handled with sticks and threads. You can walk and talk by yourself; you're just what I've always dreamed of and you'll bring me success and lots of money, you'll see.'

'Over my dead body!' said Mrs Pepperpot, who was still furious. 'I don't even remember the story of Sleeping Beauty.'

24   'I shall be telling the story,' explained the

puppet-man, 'and you just have to do the things I say. But you don't come into the first act at all, so you can stand at the side and watch the other puppets through that crack in the curtain. Now it's time for the show to start, so be a sport and stay there, won't you ?'

'I may and I mayn't,' said Mrs Pepperpot, so he lifted her gingerly down on the side of the puppet-stage which was set up in the middle of the real theatre stage.

Then the lights in the hall went out and those on the little stage went on. Mrs Pepperpot peeped through the hole in the curtain. The scene was a magnificent marble hall and she could see a puppet king and queen sitting on their thrones with their courtiers standing round. They were looking at a baby doll in a cradle.

The man began to speak behind the stage.

'There was once a king and a queen who had been blessed with a baby princess.'

'Lucky he didn't want me to lie in the cradle!' thought Mrs Pepperpot.

The man read on, telling how the good fairies were asked to the christening party and how they each gave the little princess a gift. Waving 25 their wands over her cradle the fairies came in one by one.

'May you have the gift of Beauty!' said one.

'May you have the gift of Patience!' said another.

'I could certainly do with that gift,' said Mrs Pepperpot to herself. 'If there's anything I lack it's patience!'

When all the good fairies except one had waved their wands over the cradle, there was a terrible clap of thunder and the stage went completely dark for a moment.

'Goodness Gracious!' cried Mrs Pepperpot, 'I hope they haven't had a break-down!' She was beginning to get excited about the play now.

The lights came on again, and there was the bad fairy leaning over the baby with her wand.

'Ha, ha!' said the puppet-man in an old witch sort of voice. 'Today you are all happy, but this is *my* gift to the princess; in your fifteenth year may you prick your finger on a spindle and die!' And with that the bad fairy vanished in another clap of thunder and black-out.

'Well, if I'm the Sleeping Beauty, I'm a good deal more than fifteen years old and I'm still hale and hearty!' thought Mrs Pepperpot.

The puppet-man had now brought on another fairy to tell the king and queen that their daughter would not really die, but only go into a long, long sleep.

'One day a prince will come and wake her up,' said the fairy and that was the end of the first act.

The puppet-man was glad to see Mrs Pepperpot still standing there, but he didn't take any chances and caught her up roughly before she could protest. No matter how much she wriggled, she was dressed in the princess's blonde wig with a crown on top and a veil down her back. The worst part was when the puppet-man made up her face: Ough! It tasted like candle grease!

But when at last he put her down in front of a little mirror, she had to admit she looked rather wonderful.

'Now listen,' said the puppet-man. 'I don't mind if you make up your own speeches, but you must follow the story as I tell it, and one thing you must remember; no advertising! It's strictly forbidden on this TV station.'

'Is it indeed!' said Mrs Pepperpot, who had not forgiven him for the rough treatment she had had — why, he'd even pulled her hair! 'We'll see about that!' she muttered.

But there was no time to argue, as the puppet-man was preparing to raise the curtain again. The scene was the same as before, but at first it was empty of puppets while the puppet-man read the introduction to the next part of the story.

'The king was so anxious to keep his only child safe from all harm, that he ordered every spindle in the country to be burned and forbade any more to be made. Meanwhile the princess grew up with all the gifts she had received from the fairies; she was good and beautiful, modest and patient, and everyone loved her. Then one day when she was fifteen years old the king and queen had gone out and she was all alone in the palace. She thought she would explore a bit.'

The puppet-man stopped reading and whispered to Mrs Pepperpot: 'This is where you come in! Walk across the marble hall and up the winding staircase in the corner. You'll find the witch at the top, spinning.'

He gave her a little push, and Mrs Pepperpot, in all her princess finery, walked on to the stage as grandly as she could. In the middle of the marble hall she stood still and looked for the staircase. When she saw it she turned to the audi-

ence and, pointing to the stairs, she said: 'I have

to go up there; I hope it's safe! Always buy planks at Banks, the lumber man!' And up she went, holding her long skirt like a lady.

At the top of the stairs she found the witch puppet sitting, turning her spindle in her hand.

'Why, whatever are you doing with that old-fashioned thing?' asked Mrs Pepperpot.

'I am spinning,' said the puppet-man in his old witch voice.

'I call that silly,' said Mrs Pepperpot, 'when you can buy the best knitting wool in town at Lamb's Wool Shop!'

The audience laughed at this, but the puppet-man was not amused. However, he couldn't stop now, so he went on with the play, saying in his old witch voice: 'Would you like to spin, my child?'

'I don't mind if I do,' said Mrs Pepperpot. As she took the spindle from the witch's hand, the puppet-man whispered to her to pretend to prick herself.

'Ouch!' cried Mrs Pepperpot, sucking her finger and shaking it, 'I need a plaster from Mr Sands, the chemist!'

Again the audience laughed. The puppet-man now whispered to her to lie down on the bed to sleep. She asked if he wanted her to snore to make it more life-like.

'Of course not!' he said angrily, 'and I don't want any advertising for sleeping pills either!'

'Not necessary!' said Mrs Pepperpot, making herself comfortable on the bed. Then she raised her head for a moment and in a sing-song voice she spoke to the people in the audience.

> *The moment you recline*
> *On a mattress from Irvine*
> *You will fall into a sleep*
> *That is really quite divine!*

The puppet-man had difficulty in getting himself heard through the shouts of laughter that greeted this outrageous poem. But at last he was able to go on with the story how the princess slept for a hundred years and everyone in the palace slept too. When he got to the bit about the rose-hedge growing thicker and thicker round the walls of the palace, Mrs Pepperpot popped her head up again and said:

> *Quick-growing roses*
30      *From Ratlin and Moses.*

and then pretended to sleep again. She was really getting her revenge on the puppet-man, and she was enjoying every minute of it.

The puppet-man struggled on, but now the audience laughed at everything that was said, and he began to wonder if he should stop the show. He tried reading again: 'At length the king's son came to the narrow stairs in the tower. When he reached the top he opened the door of the little chamber, and there he saw the most beautiful sight he had ever seen – the Sleeping Beauty.'

While the gramophone played soft music to suit the scene, the puppet prince walked up the stairs and came through the door. Mrs Pepperpot winked one eye at the audience and said:

> *I owe my beautiful skin*
> *To Complexion-Milk by Flyn.*

The puppet prince walked stiffly over to her bed and stiffly bent down and planted a wooden kiss on her cheek. But this was too much for Mrs Pepperpot: 'No, no!' she shrieked, jumping out of bed and knocking the prince flying, so that all his threads broke and he landed in an untidy heap at the bottom of the stairs.

Down the stairs came Mrs Pepperpot herself, and, jumping over the fallen prince, she rushed across the stage and out through the curtain, while the audience rolled in their seats and clapped and shouted for the princess to come back.

But once safely in the dressing-room, Mrs Pepperpot only just had time to snatch off her wig and veil and crown before she grew to her normal size. The little things she put in her handbag and she walked through the door as calmly as you please, only to be met by the poor puppet-man, who was wringing his hands and crying even worse than before the show.

'Whatever's the matter?' asked Mrs Pepperpot.

'My show's ruined!' he wailed. 'They'll never put it on TV again after all that advertising!'

'Advertising?' Mrs Pepperpot pretended to be surprised. 'Wasn't it all part of the play?'

But the puppet-man wasn't listening to her: 'Oh dear, oh dear! What will become of me? And now I have no Sleeping Beauty at all!'

'You should treat your puppets with more respect,' said Mrs Pepperpot, 'they don't like being pushed about and having their hair pulled!'

32    With that she left him and walked out to the

square to get on the bus. Her friends had all been too busy laughing and discussing the play to notice that she hadn't been with them. She sat down next to Sarah South who asked her if she had enjoyed the show.

'Oh, I had a lovely time! We all did, I mean!' said Mrs Pepperpot.

A few days later the puppet-man was mending the threads of his puppet-prince. He was feeling happier now, because all the newspapers had written that his way of playing Sleeping Beauty was new and original, and they all praised his performance very highly.

There was a knock on the door and the postman handed him a small parcel. He wondered what it could be, but when he opened it he stared with astonishment: inside was the princess's wig, crown and veil and also a reel of black thread and a little note.

The puppet-man read it aloud:

> *As back to you these things I send,*
> *May I be bold and recommend*
> *When next your puppet prince you mend,*
> *Try Jiffy's thread; it will not rend.*

Who had sent the parcel? And where did that little puppet go who could walk and talk on its own?

'If only I knew!' sighed the puppet-man.

# Sir Mark the Valiant

THERE was once a little boy called Mark who had to stay in bed because he had whooping cough. His friends couldn't visit him in case they too caught the whooping cough, but he didn't really mind, as he had something very special to play with.

That something special was a castle which stood on a little table by Mark's bed. It had a tower and ramparts and a moat with a draw-bridge over it, and it was made to look as if it had been built long, long ago. Actually, it was made in a modern factory, and Mark's father had bought it cheaply in a sale. But Mark hated to hear his mother tell people it was cheap; he thought it was so grand and beauti-ful, it ought to have cost lots and lots of money.

Mark also had a flag which he put on the tower and a handsome knight, dressed in white armour and riding on a white horse with a long mane and tail. The knight he called Sir Guy and he put him on the ramparts to keep a watch for enemies. The horse had its head turned a little, as if it was looking for enemies to come and attack the castle from behind.

There were many windows in the castle; in the tower, which had a winding staircase, there were narrow slits and in the top of the tower there was just one window with bars.

'That is where Sir Guy puts his prisoners,' Mark told his mother.

The little boy played with the castle all day long, and at night when his mother put it back on the table, he would lie gazing at it till he fell asleep. Sometimes the coughing would be so bad that it made his eyes water so that he saw everything through a haze; then the castle seemed to be shimmering with lights from every window – except one; the barred window in the tower was always dark.

'Sir Guy will put the light on when he puts his prisoner there,' said Mark.

One night he had been coughing and whooping so much that both his father and mother had sat with him, one holding his poor head and the other his hand. At last it stopped and he could breathe more comfortably. So his mother gave him some medicine and his father tucked him up, and then they both said good night and put out the light.

Mark was very tired; he lay there rubbing his eyes and then he looked at the castle. It looked so beautiful with the lights shimmering in every window – *every* window? Mark sat up in bed; even the barred window in the tower was lit up tonight! And what was that? Surely Sir Guy was moving? Yes, his head was moving from side to side, and now he was lifting his hand to shade his eyes, as if he was searching for something in the distance.

Now the horse moved its head too and pawed the ground with its right foreleg!

Suddenly Sir Guy dug his spurs in, galloped over the drawbridge and headed his horse straight up the counterpane towards Mark's chest! It looked as if he were riding through a flowery meadow and the horse's mane and tail were flying in the wind!

Just before they reached Mark's chin, the knight reined in his horse so that it reared on its hind legs.

'To battle! To battle!' shouted Sir Guy, drawing his sword and waving it over his head. 'Rally to me, my men!' The horse neighed loudly, reared again and waved its hooves so near to Mark's face, he thought he was going to kick 37 him. But he lay quite still, as he didn't want to frighten them away.

'Where are my men?' shouted Sir Guy. 'They have deserted me in my hour of need! Who will follow me now?' he said, and then he pointed his sword at Mark; 'Will you be my squire and fight by my side?'

'I'd like to,' said Mark, 'but who's the enemy?'

'Haven't you heard?' said the knight. 'Didn't you see the light in the prison window? I'm getting ready to capture Sir Hugh. Then I will lock him up in the tower for the rest of his life.'

'How will you find him?' asked Mark.

'A message came to me that he is on his way. But now, alas, my men have fled and I have no one to help me except you.'

'I will do my best,' Mark promised, 'but who is Sir Hugh?'

'He is the most fearsome knight in the whole land; wherever he goes he leaves terror behind, castles burned and people robbed and killed. No one has ever defeated him in battle and it is known that he is afraid of only one thing.'

'What is that?' asked Mark.

'Ah!' cried the knight, 'if we knew that the

task would be easy! But he keeps the secret well and no one knows what it is he fears!'

'Oh well,' said Mark, 'he'll have to be pretty big to frighten me!'

At that moment he heard a hollow laugh which seemed to be coming from behind the medicine bottle on the table beside his bed.

'So you're not afraid of me, eh?' It sounded more like a snarl than a voice, and before Mark could answer, a knight in shining red armour from head to foot rushed forward to the edge of the table and took a flying leap right on to the bed! Sir Guy moved a little nearer to Mark's chin.

'I heard you were looking for me, Sir Guy!' shouted Sir Hugh, waving his sword over his head. 'Well, here I am and I challenge you to battle on this plain!' And he pointed to the part of the counterpane that covered Mark's tummy.

Sir Guy had now gathered up his courage; he jumped off his horse, which trotted behind him and he ran full tilt down Mark's chest, shouting: 'Have at you, Sir Hugh, in the King's name!'

The two knights came together in a great

clash of swords. They hit each other on their helmets, breastplates and shields. Back and forth they went, and Mark watched spellbound to see which one would go down first.

Suddenly Sir Hugh's sword knocked Sir Guy down and Sir Hugh picked him up and tucked him under one arm and his horse under the other.

'Ah ha!' shouted Sir Hugh, 'I have you at my mercy!' Then he turned to Mark and shouted at him, 'I challenge you, Moonface, to come to his aid!'

Just then Mark started coughing. He whooped and he whooped and the whole bed shook like an earthquake. Sir Hugh dropped Sir Guy and his horse and they all ran this way and that, trying to find a place where the ground wasn't heaving under them!

When at last Mark stopped and everything became quiet once more, he saw both the knights pick themselves up and walk towards his face. Sir Hugh was in front and came as close as he dared. Then he said: 'Tell me, Moonface, what caused the earth to tremble? Are you a magician?'

'Oh no, sir,' answered Mark, 'I just have the whooping cough.'

Sir Hugh looked at him with horror in his eyes: 'Did you say whooping cough?'

'That's right,' said Mark, 'I've had it for a week now.'

'Who told you of my one fear in life?' thundered Sir Hugh, shaking his fists at Mark, his face almost as red as his armour.

'No one, sir,' said Mark, 'but it's a very catching illness and I'm afraid the germs will attack you any minute now.'

'Oh no!' shouted Sir Hugh as he ran full tilt to the bottom end of the bed. 'Let me get away from here!'

'If I were you, sir,' said Mark, 'I would lock myself up in a room until the danger of infection is over.'

'I will, I will!' cried Sir Hugh, whose knees were knocking inside his armour by now, he was so frightened. 'But where can I go?'

'Well,' said Mark, 'I suggest you walk across that drawbridge, open the door at the bottom of the tower, climb the winding staircase until you reach the top. There you will find a little room with bars across the window, and if you lock the door you will be quite safe.'

Before you could say knife, that knight was scurrying across the drawbridge and disappearing through the door into the tower! A moment later Mark could see his face peering through the bars of the lighted prison window!

'Hurrah!' shouted Sir Guy, who had been standing near Mark's face, watching. 'That was a master stroke! You have defeated the King's worst enemy, and for this good deed His Majesty will justly reward you!' Facing Mark and raising his sword in his right hand, Sir Guy then said: 'From the bottom of my heart I thank you and salute you, Sir Mark the Valiant!'

'It's very kind of you, sir,' said Mark, 'but I only told him about my whooping cough.'

But Sir Guy paid no attention. He was striding across the counterpane to where his horse stood. The horse whinnied as the knight swung himself into the saddle, and then it trotted quietly towards the drawbridge. Soon the knight was back in his place on the ramparts, looking into the distance in front of him, while his horse turned its head to see if there were enemies coming up from behind.

★

In the morning Mark woke up feeling better. What a strange dream he had had! He looked at the castle to see if he could see Sir Hugh peering through the bars of the lighted prison window. There on one side stood the white horse with Sir Guy on its back, just as he had left it the night before. But there was no light in any of the windows.

Mark's mother came in at that moment with his breakfast.

'Good morning, Mark!' she said, and then she looked at him more closely. 'You look *much* better today,' she said, 'the whooping cough must be nearly over.'

'Yes,' said Mark, 'we had a battle last night and I won! I am now Sir Mark the Valiant and my castle is called "Castle Valiant".'

His mother smiled and said he must have been dreaming, but Mark thought it was all too real to have been a dream.

# Mrs Pepperpot and the Brooch Hunt

THE last time Mrs Pepperpot tried her hand at playing detective you may remember she nearly ended up as mashed potato. But she still has a secret longing to be one of those smart detectives you see on the films – the kind that solve everything as easy as winking.

Meanwhile, she has decided not to arrest those potato thieves. Instead, she goes to see the family almost every day and she knows all their names. There's Mrs Grey, the mother, who tries to keep the home together. It's very difficult for her, because her husband's been out of work for many months and now he's gone to the coast to see if he can get a job on a boat. Then there's Peter, who is ten and a sensible boy, and Betty, who is eight, and little Bobby, who is only three. He keeps asking about his talking potato, and, though the other children don't know what he's talking about, Mrs Pepperpot does, so she has bought him a clockwork frog to play with instead.

Each time she visits the Greys she brings some potatoes, and she doesn't forget the hungry mouse, either; he gets a bit of bacon rind behind the door in the scullery. When she goes home the children often walk part of the way with her and talk about all sorts of things.

Once she happened to say that she had lost a little silver brooch – one she had been given as a christening present.

'I hate to lose it,' she told the children, 'because I've had it all my life and it's a pretty little thing.'

'Why don't you let us be detectives and help you find it?' Peter asked.

'Oh yes!' cried Betty, clapping her hands. 'That would be fun!'

'*I* want to be deti-deti too!' shouted Bobby, dancing up and down.

'Oh, it's hardly worth making too much fuss about,' said Mrs Pepperpot, though she secretly rather liked the idea.

'Come on, Mrs Pepperpot,' said Peter, putting on a grown-up detective sort of voice, 'tell us where you last remember seeing the lost item.'

Mrs Pepperpot smiled: 'Now, let me see; I 45

think I wore it at Nelly North's when we had a club meeting there last month.'

Peter got out a piece of paper and pencil and noted this down.

'Right,' he said, 'when can we start investigations?'

'Well,' said Mrs Pepperpot, 'I'm busy all day tomorrow with the washing, but we could meet here about four o'clock, and by then I may have thought where else I might have left it.'

'And we can work out a plan of campaign,' said Peter importantly.

So the children promised to meet Mrs Pepperpot by a certain big fir-tree on the road between their house and hers at four o'clock the next day, and they were very excited about it, especially little Bobby, who kept talking about the deti–detis till his mother put him to bed.

Next day at four o'clock sharp they all met at the tree. Mrs Pepperpot had brought a torch, because it got dark so early.

'First we'll walk over the meadow to Nelly North's Farm,' she said. 'I have an idea it might be under her sofa. She's not a very tidy person, but I don't want to offend her by hinting she hasn't cleaned her room properly, so I want you,

Peter, to take this torch and shine it under the sofa while I keep Nelly talking. You must do it secretly, mind, so that she doesn't notice.'

'What about Bobby and me?' asked Betty.

'You'll have to keep watch outside,' said Mrs Pepperpot.

So they started off across the meadow, walking in single file along a narrow path with Mrs Pepperpot in front, shining the torch. Suddenly the torch flew up in the air and Mrs Pepperpot disappeared! At least, that's what the children thought, for, of course, *we* know that she had shrunk again! The torch was still alight when it landed, but Mrs Pepperpot had rolled into the long grass, and it was Bobby who found her and picked her up by one leg!

'Here's my talking 'tato!' he shouted, dangling poor Mrs Pepperpot upside down.

'Put it down, Bobby,' said Betty, 'it might bite!'

'No!' insisted Bobby, who had now set Mrs Pepperpot on his hand. 'It's my talking 'tato!'

Mrs Pepperpot had now got her breath back, so she said as quietly as she could: 'That's right, children, Bobby *has* seen me like this before.'

'Why, it's Mrs Pepperpot!' cried Peter and Betty together. 'However did you get so small?'

'That will take too long to explain,' said Mrs Pepperpot, 'but it happens to me from time to time, and last time Bobby found me in the bottom of the potato bucket, so that's why he thinks I'm a talking potato.'

'Let *me* hold you,' said Betty. 'I'll be very careful.'

'Yes, I think I would feel a bit safer,' said Mrs Pepperpot, as Bobby was jogging her up and down in his excitement, making her quite giddy.

'What about our search? Will we have to call it off?' asked Peter.

Mrs Pepperpot didn't like to disappoint them, and she'd already thought up a new plan, but first she made them promise never to tell anybody about her turning small.

'You must hold up your right hands, as they do in the films, and swear you will never speak of this to a living soul.'

Peter and Betty held up their right hands and repeated Mrs Pepperpot's words, but little Bobby had to be told he would get a hard smack if he ever said he'd seen a talking potato!

'Now,' said Mrs Pepperpot, 'instead of me going in to talk to Nelly North, I want Peter to knock at the door. When Nelly opens it he must say that he's collecting for — let's see — a home for worn-out car tyres. If he says it quickly she won't notice, and then when she's gone to the kitchen to look for a penny, you just switch on the torch and shine it under the sofa in the front room, and if you see a shining object, bring it with you. Betty and Bobby and I will be waiting behind that tree over there.'

By now they had reached the road in front of North Farm and Mrs Pepperpot pointed her tiny hand at a tree standing a little way from the house.

'Right oh!' said Peter and walked bravely over to the door, hiding the torch in his pocket.

The others waited in the dark till he came back. It didn't take long, but Peter was quite excited when he came towards them, and he was holding something in his hand.

'Let me see!' said Mrs Pepperpot, who was standing on Betty's hand. Peter put the object down beside her and shone the torch on it.

'Oh dear!' she said, 'I'm afraid you've picked up the wrong thing. This is a silver ring that was 49 sent to Nelly from her uncle in America; she said she had lost it the day of the meeting.'

Peter's face had fallen. 'What do we do now?'

'It's no good going back, you would find it too hard to explain,' said Mrs Pepperpot. 'Put it in your pocket while we go on to Sally South's house just along the road here. That's another place I think I may have dropped my brooch when I was there for the silver-wedding party.'

So they walked on to Sally South's house, Mrs Pepperpot riding in Betty's pocket and Bobby kept putting his fingers in to see if she was still there.

Sally didn't know Peter when she opened the door to him, and she was a bit deaf, so she didn't quite catch what he was collecting for, but he looked a nice boy, so she went off for a penny from her money-box. While she was out of the room Peter got the chance to shine his torch under the furniture and even behind the grand-father clock. There he saw something glittering, so he fished it out and put it in his pocket. When Sally came back he thanked her very nicely for the penny and ran back to the others who were hiding outside.

50     'Did you find it?' whispered Betty.

'I think so,' said Peter, bringing the little thing out of his pocket.

But when she saw it Mrs Pepperpot shook her head; 'Sorry, Peter, I'm afraid that's not it either. It's a medallion Sally's husband gave her for a silver-wedding present. He was very cross when he found she had dropped it that day.'

Peter looked quite disheartened. 'This doesn't seem such a good idea, after all,' he said. 'Perhaps we'd better give it up.'

'Is that the way for Detective Sergeant Peter Grey to speak?' demanded Mrs Pepperpot, who was really enjoying the hunt, though it was true she wasn't doing the hard work! 'Let's try East Farm; Mr Pepperpot and I were there just after Christmas for the baby's christening. I was god-mother, so I carried the baby, and I expect the brooch fell off when I was putting the baby in his cot.'

'Can I carry my talking 'tato now?' asked Bobby who had been very good and quiet for a long time.

'All right, but don't you drop me now,' said Mrs Pepperpot, whose clothes and hair were getting quite messed up with all this passing from hand to hand.

When they got to East Farm only Mr East was at home, looking after the baby. He was a kindly man and never minded giving children the odd penny. So he put down his newspaper and went out to search for a coin in his jacket pocket. The baby was lying in a cot, playing with his toes. Peter remembered what Mrs Pepperpot had said about putting the baby in his cot, so when he saw a small silver bell in the cot beside the baby, he quickly picked it up and pocketed it. Mr East came in and gave him the penny, and Peter thanked him politely and ran out to the others.

'I hope I've got the right thing this time!' he cried, jingling the little bell as he pulled it out of his pocket.

'Oh, you silly boy!' exclaimed Mrs Pepperpot, 'how could you think that was my brooch? It belongs to the baby's rattle which I gave him myself for a christening present!'

Peter looked very sheepish; 'Well, you see, I don't really know what a brooch *is*!'

'Why didn't you say so before?' Mrs Pepperpot was beginning to get cross. 'A detective needs to know what he's looking for!'

'*I* know what a brooch is,' said Betty, 'it has a

pin which fits into a clasp and you put it in your shawl.'

'That's right,' said Mrs Pepperpot who was trying hard to think where else they could search. 'I've got it. I'm sure I wore it for Paul West's confirmation. It was pouring with rain that day and I took my umbrella; I bet it dropped into the umbrella stand at West Farm. Come along, children, if it isn't there we'll go home, I promise you.'

So they turned about and trudged down a little lane till they got to West Farm. Peter knocked, as before, but this time there was no answer, so he tried the handle and the door opened. There, just inside, was the umbrella stand Mrs Pepperpot had told him about, so he quickly shone his torch right down to the bottom of it, and, Goodness Gracious! there he could see a small pin with what looked like the letter 'P' on it! Surely that must be it, thought Peter and made a dive for it. Then he ran out to the others, hoping no one had heard him.

This time they were hiding behind a shed and Peter made sure he was out of sight of the house before he opened his hand: 'There,' he said, 'I've got it!'

'Show me,' said Mrs Pepperpot, but then she almost cried: 'This isn't my brooch – it's a tie-pin!'

'But it had "P" on it, so I thought it must be Pepperpot!' stammered poor Peter.

'I wasn't *christened* Pepperpot, was I? I only married him! The "P" stands for Paul who was confirmed that day. Goodness, how careless everybody is with their belongings!'

There was nothing for it now; they would have to give up and go home. What bothered Mrs Pepperpot was how to return all those things to their rightful owners. For once she really hadn't been very clever.

The three children were tired and walking slowly along the road, Betty holding Mrs Pepperpot, when suddenly they heard running footsteps coming in their direction.

'They're after us!' squeaked Mrs Pepperpot. 'Run, children!'

In their fright the children nearly fell over each other and poor Mrs Pepperpot was thrown right over the ditch into the field.

The footsteps were coming nearer.

'Stop, thief!' shouted someone. It was Nelly North. 'I can see them.'

'There's the boy!' shouted Sally South who was following her.

Mr East was plodding behind with fat Mrs West. 'Come on, boy,' he shouted, 'you might as well give up!'

The children were crying by now and little Bobby stumbled over a stone and fell.

At that moment a small but commanding voice came through the air. 'Hands up or I shoot!' it shouted. It seemed to be coming from nowhere and everyone stood stock still. Then it spoke again: 'This is the secret police calling with a message for the following people: Mrs North, Mrs South, Mr East and Mrs West. Stand by please! Can you hear me?'

They were all so surprised to hear their names called, that they very meekly answered 'Yes'.

'Right,' went on the voice. 'You can all expect a surprise in your letter-boxes tomorrow morning. On one condition, that you immediately go home and leave the children alone!'

The children had stopped running too, and watched with amazement as, one by one, Nelly North, Sally South, Mr East and fat Mrs West all turned about and walked away without a single look behind them.

'Phew!' said a voice right beside the children. There stood Mrs Pepperpot, as large as life. She was holding a dock-leaf in her hand and it was curled in the shape of a large cone.

'What's that for?' asked little Bobby who had picked himself up and was *very* pleased to see his friend Mrs Pepperpot again.

'The secret police always carry loudspeakers!' she answered, smiling at the children. Then they all went home to her house and had nice hot cocoa and pancakes.

Next morning when Nelly North looked in her letterbox she found the silver ring she had lost, Sally South found her silver medallion, Mr East found the silver bell from the baby's rattle and Mrs West found her son's tie-pin. They certainly were surprised!

But the one who was most surprised was Mrs Pepperpot. When she opened her letter-box she found a little parcel in it, and inside was her brooch. There was also a note from Peter, which said:

Dear Mrs Pepperpot,
   After the clue you gave us last night, your detectives have been able to solve the mystery. We have

put your potato-bucket back in its place in the potato-field. Thank you.

Yours truly,
Detective Sergeant P. Grey

'Of course!' said Mrs Pepperpot to herself, 'I was wearing the brooch on the night when the potato thieves came, and I must have dropped it in the bucket!'

# Penguin Children's 60s